# TRUST YOURSELF

## IT'S OK TO JUST SAY NO!

WRITTEN BY JANIS HUNT

Illustrated by: Bethany Smith

Emma really loved her mom.
She loved how she was always calm.
She loved when they would sit and read.
She loved to help her pull the weeds.
When evening came, then they would play.
She even taught her to crochet.

As years went by and Emma grew,
Her mom taught her more things to do.
She taught her how to fly a kite.
She taught her how to be polite.

Be kind and ask permission first.
Listen, smile with no outbursts.
Say please and thank you. Don't tell lies.
And always share so no one cries.
But even though you're very small,
Remember this, the most of all:

If you've been taught to be polite,
But something doesn't feel quite right,
Trust yourself and don't delay.
It's all right to walk away.
As soon as it feels wrong, say so.
It's OK to just say no!

Emma looked with some concern.
"Is this what children always learn?
When are times I should say no?
What are times that I should go?"

Her mom said, "Turn the page and see
Why others teach this just like me."

Grace was with friends in a store.
She'd shopped with these friends once before.
One friend said, "Let's hide these toys.
We'll sneak them out. We won't make noise."

Grace soon had an awful feeling.
She never wanted to be stealing.
Her mom had taught her what to do.
She thought it over through and through:

If you've been taught to be polite,
But something doesn't feel quite right,
Trust yourself and don't delay.
It's all right to walk away.
As soon as it feels wrong, say so.
It's OK to just say no!

Grace said, "This I will not do."
And, "I'm surprised at both of you!"
Grace told them that they were wrong.
They really knew it all along.

Aashi's family celebrations
Filled each room with generations.
Uncles, grandpas, aunts and more,
Cousins piled up on the floor.
Tables full of tasty snacks,
On fancy dishes with no cracks.

Aashi loved the fun and chasing,
But she hated the embracing.
Tickling, pinching, being kissed,
These are things she tried to miss.
"Sit on my lap. Come hug me."
Aashi longed to just be free.

But this time when they called her over,
Saying, "Please come even closer!"
Her mom had taught her what to do.
She thought it over through and through:

If you've been taught to be polite,
But something doesn't feel quite right,
Trust yourself and don't delay.
It's all right to walk away.
As soon as it feels wrong, say so.
It's OK to just say no!

Aashi said "I love you dearly,
But please listen to me clearly.
I am leaving now to play."
And then she turned and walked away.

Yuzuki met friends at the pool.
To swim with them, she thought was cool.
But it was always just assumed
That they would all change in one room.

This would sometimes make her shy.
(And really, she did not know why.)
No one else did seem to care,
At least not that she was aware.
Her mom had taught her what to do.
She thought it over through and through:

If you've been taught to be polite,
But something doesn't feel quite right,
Trust yourself and don't delay.
It's all right to walk away.
As soon as it feels wrong, say so.
It's OK to just say no!

Yuzuki looked and found a place,
A bathroom that was her own space.
She told her friends she would return.
And not one seemed the least concerned.

Ruth was walking home from school.
"Come straight home!" was her mom's rule.
A car pulled up. She heard her name.
She thought this must just be a game.

But then she recognized her coach.
He slowed way down as he approached.
"I'll take you home. Get in my car.
I know that it's not very far."

Her parents liked him quite a lot.
And yet her stomach tied in knots.
She didn't like him. That was clear.
And lately he was always near.
Her mom had taught her what to do.
She thought it over through and through:

If you've been taught to be polite,
But something doesn't feel quite right,
Trust yourself and don't delay.
It's all right to walk away.
As soon as it feels wrong, say so.
It's OK to just say no!

Ruth said, "Thank you. I'll just walk.
I really don't have time to talk."
She would not get inside his car.
She ran right home. It wasn't far.

Jin was friends with lots of boys.
They played and teased and shared their toys.
But sometimes one would push and shove
Or grab her, which she did not love.
Her mom had taught her what to do.
She thought it over through and through:

If you've been taught to be polite,
But something doesn't feel quite right,
Trust yourself and don't delay.
It's all right to walk away.
As soon as it feels wrong, say so.
It's OK to just say no!

Jin said, "You must stop this now!
These are things I won't allow!"
They said, "Sorry. We were wrong."
They should have known that all along.

Isabelle went to a park.
She had to be home before dark.
A man came up with urgency.
He said, "It's an emergency!"

"Your mother needs you right away.
There's no more time for you to play.
Come with me as she has asked.
I'll help you get home really fast."

Isabelle thought hard and long.
She really thought this must be wrong.
Her mom would never send this stranger.
Everything made her feel danger.
Her mom had taught her what to do.
She thought it over through and through:

**If you've been taught to be polite,
But something doesn't feel quite right,
Trust yourself and don't delay.
It's all right to walk away.
As soon as it feels wrong, say so.
It's OK to just say no!**

Isabelle said, "I won't go.
You are someone I don't know."
She backed away and did not stop.
She must have run about five blocks.
When she got home she told her mother,
Father, sister and her brother.

Fajah loved to sing on Sunday.
"Church was fun", she often would say.
Meetings there, some were for kids,
(Except the ones that sleep in cribs.)

The pastor knew them all by name.
It seemed he loved them just the same.
But sometimes after the big service,
Fajah would get really nervous.
He would call them to his office.
This made Fajah's stomach nauseous.

She didn't like to go alone
And meet the pastor on her own.
Her mom had taught her what to do.
She thought it over through and through:

If you've been taught to be polite,
But something doesn't feel quite right,
Trust yourself and don't delay.
It's all right to walk away.
As soon as it feels wrong, say so.
It's OK to just say no!

So this time when he called her in
And tummy rumblings did begin,
She said, "I'd like to bring my friend."
And she had one to recommend.
He said, "I think that's fine and dandy."
And on his desk were jars of candy.

Aiyana loved to be with friends.
Just what they did, it would depend,
But sleeping over was the best.
She liked that better than the rest.

Once while waiting for the movie
Someone whispered, "You're a beauty."
He's a brother, she presumed.
And then he asked her to his room.

She suddenly felt tense inside.
It almost made her want to hide.
Her mom had taught her what to do.
She thought it over through and through:

If you've been taught to be polite,
But something doesn't feel quite right,
Trust yourself and don't delay.
It's all right to walk away.
As soon as it feels wrong, say so.
It's OK to just say no!

Aiyana said, "I'd rather not."
She told him "No," right on the spot.
Something hadn't felt quite right
She walked away out of his sight.

Kaleah and Kit played on the floor.
Kit's mom whispered through the door.
"Kaleah dear, you should get going.
Outside streetlights all are glowing."

Darkness meant that it was late.
Kaleah guessed it must be eight.
Soon the house had quite a crowd.
And everyone got very loud.

Suddenly they heard a sound.
Someone fell hard on the ground.
Kaleah watched him try to stand.
Alcohol was in his hand.

He turned and offered her a ride.
Kaleah's eyes got very wide.
Her mom had taught her what to do.
She thought it over through and through:

If you've been taught to be polite,
But something doesn't feel quite right,
Trust yourself and don't delay.
It's all right to walk away.
As soon as it feels wrong, say so.
It's OK to just say no!

"Thank you, but I'll call my mother!
If she can't, I'll call another!"
Kaleah knew to not permit
Someone to drive who was not fit.

One afternoon when school was done,
Ella took off in a run.
Her cousin was to babysit.
She liked him lots, she did admit.
They watched TV. They took a hike.
They ate some treats. They rode their bikes.

When they got back, he grabbed his phone.
She did not like what she was shown.
He said, "You must now promise me.
Don't tell your mom! You must agree!"
Her mom had taught her what to do.
She thought it over through and through:

**If you've been taught to be polite,
But something doesn't feel quite right,
Trust yourself and don't delay.
It's all right to walk away.
As soon as it feels wrong, say so.
It's OK to just say no!**

"I will not promise not to tell.
I know that's wrong. I know it well."
When Ella's mom got home that day,
She knew exactly what to say.

Online doing work for school,
Mia followed all the rules.
Messaging her classmates some,
Texting friends and having fun.
When suddenly inside their loop,
An unknown person joined their group.
First, he sent them funny stickers.
Then he asked them to send pictures.

Mia felt bad feelings growing.
"This feels wrong. Where is this going?"
Her mom had taught her what to do.
She thought it over through and through:

If you've been taught to be polite,
But something doesn't feel quite right,
Trust yourself and don't delay.
It's all right to walk away.
As soon as it feels wrong, say so.
It's OK to just say no!

Mia blocked this conversation,
Changed her codes and information.
First her phone, then her laptop,
She asked for help to make it stop.

All her friends, they did the same.
They did not even know his name.
Never talk online with strangers.
There are way too many dangers.

When Zenaib was at school one day,
She met some girls when out to play.
The girls told Zenaib, “Play this trick!
We think it will be really slick.
Fool your friend and we’ll agree
That in our cool crowd you can be.”

Zenaib smiled but soon felt bad.
She thought her friend would feel so sad.
Her mom had taught her what to do.
She thought it over through and through:

If you’ve been taught to be polite,
But something doesn’t feel quite right,
Trust yourself and don’t delay.
It’s all right to walk away.
As soon as it feels wrong, say so.
It’s OK to just say no!

Zenaib said “I won’t do that.
I do not want to be a brat.”
She went to play with other friends.
And this is how this story ends.

Emma learned so much that's new.
She thought it over through and through.
Now all these girls know what to do.
Their moms taught them!
And they've taught you!

IT'S ALL RIGHT TO WALK AWAY
AS SOON AS IT FEELS WRONG, SAY SO
IT'S OK TO JUST SAY NO.

For my Grandchildren

Love- Grandma Sugar

PRINT ISBN: 978-0-578-86639-0
EBOOK ISBN: 978-0-578-86644-4